Ready Steady Go!

By Celia O'Donovan (PhD)
Pat Preedy (PhD)

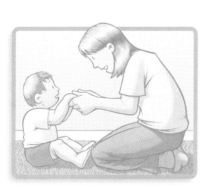

For parents and carers of young children:
A fun movement programme to develop **your** child's learning

First published in 2006
Learning Works International Ltd

Telephone +44 (0) 1672 512914
Fascimile +44 (0) 1672 519025

E-mail info@learning-works.org.uk
www.learning-works.org.uk

©2006 Learning Works

British Library Cataloguing-in-Publication Data
A Catalogue record of this book and CD is available from the British Library
ISBN 0 9531 0553 9
Printed by Xpedient UK Ltd
Designed by SLD*design*
Illustrated by Simon Walmesley

Music arranged by Andre Pysanczyn
Singer Amy Cullum
Guitarist Andre Pysanczyn
Recorded at The Music Workshop, Devizes
Recording Engineer Pete Lamb

Video recorded at Wiltshire Media studios, Devizes
Filmed and edited by Roger Calcutt
CD master prepared by James Carmichael, Take1Records, York

Ready Steady Go! is the first publication in the **Fit For Learning** series edited by Fil Came, Learning Works.

About the authors

Dr. Celia O'Donovan has wide experience as a university lecturer, researcher and nursery inspector. She is currently an educational consultant and has recently published a book on movement and learning.

Dr. Pat Preedy has worked in education for over 25 years. As headteacher of a Beacon School and a Professor at Curtin University, (Western Australia), she has developed whole brain learning techniques including a daily physical exercise programme. Currently she is an Executive Principal and Director of Research and Training for Global Education Management Systems (GEMS).

Celia and Pat have pursued a shared interest in the link between movement and brain development through the Institute of Neuro-Physiological Psychology (INPP). They have collaborated on a number of projects as well as training teachers and early years specialists in the INPP movement programme.

"Thank you for investing in our book. We know that babies and children need a balance of physical movement, healthy nutrition, love and care. We have designed this practical programme for you to use and enjoy with your child as part of giving him or her the best possible start in life."

Why Grandma Knew Best

Ready, Steady, Go! will help you to build the foundations for later learning by combining what Grandma instinctively knew with the latest research into how children learn.

We now realise the importance of traditional games, songs, rhymes and stories and an active childhood based upon secure and loving relationships.

Physical movement is essential to a child's emotional and intellectual development.
Doing this fun programme for 5 to 10 minutes each day will help your child to develop:

- body awareness;
- muscle tone;
- balance;
- body control;
- grip and finger movements;
- hand – eye co-ordination.

Each session is a golden opportunity for you to deepen the bond with your child so that he or she receives the best possible start in life.

Contents

Be safe. Be sure. Be kind.

○ Seek advice from your Health Visitor or GP before beginning the programme.

○ Never leave your baby or child unattended during the sessions.

The publishers and authors assume no responsibility or liability for any injury, loss or damage incurred as a result of any use or reliance upon the information contained in this publication.

How to Use the Ready, Steady, Go! Book

The book is in five sections:

- **Ready** – for younger babies;
- **Steady** – for older babies;
- **Go** – for toddlers and young children;
- **Getting the right balance** – milestones and advice;
- **Keeping going** – useful information and further reading.

Choose a relaxed time, setting aside 5 to 10 minutes each day. If you have twins or higher multiples, try to arrange an individual 5 minute session with each child. This will help you both to develop a close and special relationship.

Select two or three of the exercises from the appropriate section.

As information is received from sensors all over the body, your child will need bare feet and unrestrictive clothing. Remove any jewellery from you or your child and ensure that fingernails have no rough edges.

Talk with your child and make eye contact at the beginning and end of each session. Rhymes have been included throughout the book for you to sing with your child as you are doing the exercises. Do use the CD to accompany the sessions. You will rapidly notice your child's anticipation and enjoyment as the music starts to play.

Each child is different and develops at his or her own pace. During each session it is important to follow your child's natural movements without any force or pressure, taking care to gently support the head and neck when necessary.

Stop the session if your child is unhappy. You can always try again later.

Do not do the exercises with your child if he or she:

- is unwell or injured;
- has undergone recent surgery;
- is under medical supervision;
- has recently been vaccinated.

How to Use the Ready, Steady, Go! CD

The CD accompanying this book contains original versions of traditional nursery rhymes especially written for you to use during your **Ready, Steady, Go!** sessions. It has been designed for use on a CD player and home computer. More information can be found on pages 32 and 33.

Each track starts with the words and music of the nursery rhyme and is then followed by the music only. This has been done to help you time each exercise and also to encourage participation by you and your child.

The following is a summary of the CD's contents and how to access the information.

Contents of **Ready, Steady, Go!** CD	CD player	Computer
1. Music tracks for RSG sessions	✓	✓
2. Meet the authors – video demonstration		✓
3. Ideas and play suggestions for you and your toddler		✓
4. Websites for parents		✓

Using a CD player

Insert the CD and select the track(s) you wish to use in your RSG session. The music tracks have been recorded in the order used in the book. You will find the track number on the relevant exercise page or listed at the back of the book.

Using a Personal Computer

Insert the CD into your computer's DVD/CD drive. Allow a few seconds for the menu to appear on your screen. Follow the instructions to play the music tracks, video or other parts of the disc.

Use the following method if the CD does not run.

Click on Start, Run, then type in: D:\setup.exe (substitute D for the letter of your DVD/CD drive if different) then click on OK.

Most of these movements are done on a mat or rug on the floor. Each session should last about five minutes.

At the start and end of each session:

Lie your baby on his or her back. Looking into the eyes, talk softly and sing a nursery rhyme.

Movement

Choose two of these movements to do with your baby each day. Smile, talk or sing with your baby during the movements.

Rock-a-Bye

An exercise to develop your child's sense of balance.

Cradle your baby in your arms. Supporting the head, gently rock your baby from side to side, forwards and backwards and up and down.

Hold your baby over your shoulder. Supporting the head, gently rock forwards and backwards and from side to side.

Repeat several times for as long as your baby is happy with the movement.

Rock-a-bye baby on the tree top,
When the wind blows, the cradle will rock,
When the bough breaks the cradle will fall,
Down will come baby, cradle and all.

CD tracks 1 & 2

Ready 2

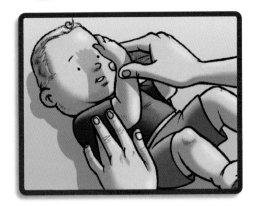

Hello Baby
. . . .
An exercise to develop your child's body awareness.

Lie your baby on his or her back. Support one arm and gently and very lightly pat underneath the arm from the shoulder to the hand.

Guide your baby's hand to his or her face and then do gentle stroking movements.

Repeat with the other arm.

Pat - a – cake,
Pat - a – cake,
Baker's man,
Bake me a cake as fast as you can.

Pat it,
and prick it,
and mark it with "B",
and put it in the oven for baby and me.

Ready 3

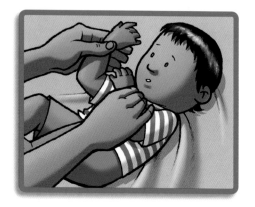

Look and Learn

An exercise to develop your child's hand-eye co-ordination and body awareness.

Lie your baby on his or her back. Hold your baby's hand and slowly move it in towards his or her eyes and then back again 2 – 3 times. Repeat with the other hand.

Hold both hands and slowly move towards his or her eyes and then back again. Repeat 2 – 3 times.

Leaving your baby on his or her back, gently hold the hands above his or her chest. Extend the arms up towards you and then out to each side at shoulder level. Bring the arms back to the centre and repeat 4 – 5 times.

Two little dicky birds sitting on a wall,
One named Peter,
And one named Paul.
Fly away Peter,
Fly away Paul.
Come back Peter,
Come back Paul.

CD tracks 5 & 6

Ready 4

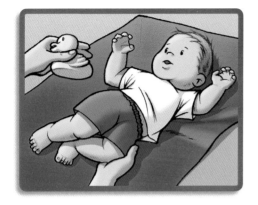

Roly Poly

An exercise to develop your child's muscle tone and body awareness.

Lie your baby on his or her back. Place a toy well out of reach on one side. Gently bend his or her leg up and help him or her to roll over and over towards the toy.

Place the toy well out of reach on the other side and do the roll the other way.

There were ten in the bed,
And the little one said,
"Roll over!
Roll over!"
So they all rolled over,
And one fell out,
There were nine in the bed,
And the little one said ....

CD tracks 7 & 8

See Saw

An exercise to develop your child's sense of balance and body control.

Sit or prop up your baby on the floor. Kneel in front so that your baby can grip your fingers.

Gently and slowly rock backwards and forwards and side to side several times.

If your baby is enjoying this, add circular movements in both directions.

See saw Margery Daw,
Johnny shall have a new master.
He shall earn but a penny a day,
Because he can't work any faster.

CD tracks 9 & 10

● Ready 6

Creepy Crawly 1
. . . .
An exercise to develop your child's muscle tone and sense of balance.

Babies need lots of opportunities to crawl. Place your baby on his or her front and encourage him or her to move across the room towards a toy.

If necessary, support the lower part of the body so that he or she can reach for the toy.

Clippety Clop!
. . . .
An exercise to develop your child's sense of balance.

Sit your baby on your lap. Gently bounce up and down, from side to side and backwards and forwards singing the following song.

Ride a cock horse to Banbury Cross,
To see a fine lady upon a white horse.
Rings on her fingers and bells on her toes,
She shall have music wherever she goes.

Steady 1

These sessions are for babies who have developed head control, can sit up and are getting ready to crawl. Each session should last five to ten minutes.

At the start and end of each session:

Support your baby-sitting on your lap. Looking into the eyes, talk softly and sing a nursery rhyme, moving in time to the tune.

Movement

Choose two or three of these movements to do with your baby each day. Smile, talk or sing with your baby during the movements.

Baby Bird

An exercise to develop your child's body control, muscle tone, grip and finger movements.

Lie your baby on his or her front. Kneel in front of your baby and let him or her grip your hands.

Gently and slowly raise and lower the upper half of the baby's body. Repeat several times.

Wheelbarrow

An exercise to develop your child's muscle tone and body control.

Lie your baby on his or her front. Place a toy just out of reach in front. Kneel behind, supporting the chest and both legs under the thighs. Gently raise up the lower half of your baby's body so that the hands and arms are taking some of the weight.

Encourage and help your baby to move forwards towards the toy.

Steady 2

Rock and Roll

An exercise to develop your child's sense of balance.

Make a roll with foam rubber or improvise with a cot blanket or bath towel. Place a colourful toy in front of the roll.

Place your baby on his or her knees with hands over the roll. Gently support under the knees and thighs.

Gently and slowly move your baby forwards over the roll towards the toy so that the arms support the front part of the body. Slowly roll back again and repeat several times.

London Bridge is falling down,
Falling down, falling down,
London Bridge is falling down,
My fair lady.

Build it up with wood and clay,
Wood and clay, wood and clay,
Build it up with wood and clay,
My fair lady.

Steady 3

Touch and Count

An exercise to develop your child's body awareness.

Lie your baby on his or her back. Using your fingertips, on one side, gently touch the toes, feet, legs, tummy, chest, neck, chin, hands and fingers, arms, shoulders, neck, ears, mouth, cheek, forehead. Count one to three over and over as you touch.

Repeat on the other side.

Lie your baby on his or her front. Using your fingertips, on one side, gently touch toes, feet, legs, hips, palms of hands, fingertips, arms, back of the neck, ears. Count one to three over and over as you touch.

Hickory, dickory dock,
The mouse ran up the clock,
The clock struck one,
The mouse ran down,
Hickory, dickory, dock.

One, two, three, four, five,
Once I caught a fish alive.
Six, seven, eight, nine, ten,
Then I let him go again.
Why did you let him go?
Because he bit my finger so!
Which finger did he bite?
This little finger on the right.

Steady 4

Riding My Bike

An exercise to develop your child's body control and body awareness.

Lie your baby on his or her back. Support the legs under the knees. Gently bend the knees towards the chest then gently extend the legs back out.

Repeat 2 – 3 times.

Now bend and extend each leg separately.

Repeat 4 – 5 times.

Place your hands on the soles of your baby's feet. Gently push and release each foot alternately 4 - 5 times. If your baby is enjoying this, rotate each leg alternately in both directions and then both legs together.

Bobby Shaftoe's gone to sea,
Silver buckles on his knee.
He'll come back and marry me,
Bonny Bobby Shaftoe.

Steady 5

Left Right

An exercise to develop your child's grip, finger movements and body awareness.

Lie your baby on his or her back. Kneel in front, letting your baby grip your fingers.

Slowly and gently stretch both arms back behind the head then move the arms forwards. Repeat 3 – 4 times.

Then slowly and gently move the arms alternately.

Gently bend up your baby's right leg and bring the left hand to touch the knee. Repeat the movement several times.

Repeat with the left leg and right hand.

Polly put the kettle on,
Polly put the kettle on,
Polly put the kettle on,
We'll all have tea.
Sukey take it off again,
Sukey take it off again,
Sukey take it off again,
They've all gone away.

CD tracks 21 & 22

Go 1

These sessions are for young children who are able to walk. Each session should last five to ten minutes.

At the start and end of each session:

Sing a nursery rhyme encouraging your child to join in and do movements such as clapping.

Movement

Choose three of these movements to do each day. Gently help, support and encourage your child during the session.

Copy Cat

An exercise to develop your child's body awareness.

With your right hand, touch and name different parts of your body from head to toe. Get your child to copy each time on his or her own body, giving help if necessary.

Repeat with the left hand and then both hands together.

Jack and Jill

An exercise to develop your child's body awareness.

Ask your child to close his or her eyes.

Jack and Jill went up the hill,
(Gently touch different parts on the left side.)

To fetch a pail of water.
(Gently touch different parts on the right side.)

Jack fell down and broke his crown,
(Gently brush down the left arm.)

And Jill came tumbling after.
(Gently brush down the right arm.)

Repeat, touching both sides at the same time.

Roundabout

An exercise to develop your child's sense of balance.

Kneel or stand in front of your child and help him or her to stand holding your hands. Gently and very slowly move round in a complete circle encouraging your child to move round with you.

Go first one way and then the other.

Ring a ring o' roses,
A pocket full of posies,
A-tish-oo, A-tish-oo,
We all fall down.

Ashes in the water,
Ashes in the sea,
We all jump up with a
One, two, three.

CD tracks 23 & 24

Go 3

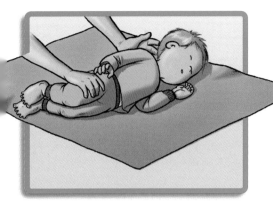

Sausage Roll

An exercise to develop your child's sense of balance.

Place a bath towel on soft flooring. Gently roll your child over and over from one end to the other and then back again.

Encourage him or her to do this independently.

Creepy Crawly 2

An exercise to develop your child's muscle tone, body control and hand-eye co-ordination.

Make an obstacle course for your child to crawl SLOWLY round. For example, along a mat, through a tunnel made with a rug draped over two chairs, round some toys placed in a zigzag, over a roll.

 **Go 4**

Row Boat

An exercise to develop your child's sense of balance.

Get your child to sit on a mat. Sit in front of your child holding both hands. Gently and slowly rock backwards and forwards and from side to side three or four times.

Repeat with the eyes closed and then standing.

 Row, row, row your boat,
Gently down the stream.

Merrily, merrily, merrily, merrily,
Life is but a dream.

Repeat

 CD tracks 25 & 26

Go 5

Bouncy Ball

An exercise to develop your child's sense of balance.

Stand in front of your child holding both hands.

Help your child to jump up and down 5 – 10 times counting with him or her.

Repeat with the eyes closed.

Half a pound of tuppenny rice,
Half a pound of treacle,
Mix it up and make it nice.
POP!
Goes the weasel.

Go 6

Straight Forward

An exercise to develop your child's body control.

Kneel in front of your child holding both hands. Help him or her to stand still for a count of 5.

Move away and encourage your child to walk in a straight line towards you. Hold the hands again and help him or her to walk backwards.

As your child develops, encourage him or her to stand still without help. Increase the distance between you, getting him or her to tiptoe, hop or jump as well as walk.

Squeaker

An exercise to develop your child's grip and finger movements.

Get a small, soft squeaky ball.

Encourage your child to squeeze the ball 5 – 10 times with each hand.

Hippity Hop

An exercise to develop your child's sense of balance, muscle tone, body control and body awareness.

Stand with feet apart and arms stretched out wide to each side at shoulder height. Look straight ahead then close your eyes. Count slowly to five and then open your eyes.

Diddle diddle dumpling, my son John,

(Hop on one leg.)

Went to bed with his trousers on.

(Hop on the other leg.)

One shoe off,

(Lift one leg bending your knee to the front.)

And one shoe on.

(Lift the other leg bending your knee to the front.)

Diddle diddle dumpling, my son John.

(Run on the spot.)

Stand with your feet together and arms by your side. Look straight ahead then close your eyes. Count slowly backwards from five to zero.

Go 8

Circle Time

An exercise to develop your child's sense of balance, body control and hand-eye co-ordination.

Hold hands, moving round in a circle one way and then the other singing the following song.

> Here we go round the Mulberry Bush,
> The Mulberry Bush,
> The Mulberry Bush.
> Here we go round the Mulberry Bush on a cold and frosty morning.

Then sing the following while doing the movements.

> This is the way we clap our hands......
> This is the way we nod our heads.......
> This is the way we shake our legs.......
> This is the way we sit on the floor.......

Close your eyes and quietly count up to five and back down to zero.

CD tracks **29** & **30**

Go 9

Quick March

An exercise to develop your child's body awareness, muscle tone, balance, grip and finger movements.

Sing 'The Grand Old Duke of York' with the following actions.

Oh the Grand old Duke of York,
(March on the spot.)

He had 10 000 men.
(Hold up 10 fingers splayed.)

He marched them up to the top of the hill,
And he marched them down again.
(March knees high, arms swinging.)

When they were up, they were up.
(Stretch up high, fingers splayed.)

When they were down, they were down.
(Crouch down, touching the floor with the finger tips.)

When they were only half way up,
(Come up half way.)

They were neither up,
(Stretch up.)

Nor down.
(Curl down.)

Getting the Right Balance

Growing up

Each child is special and unique and as a parent or carer you have a vital role to play. Babies and children need a balance of:

- physical movement and stimulation;
- healthy nutrition;
- love and care.

Although development follows a sequence, the precise age for each milestone may vary.

From birth, babies are able to use all of their senses and can freely move their arms and legs. The neck muscles are not strong enough to control head movement so care has to be taken to support the head.

During the first six months a baby develops head control and focus. He or she learns to:

- roll over;
- sit with support;
- reach and grab.

Between 6 and 9 months babies learn to:

- use their hands to support their body and head when lying on their stomach;
- sit unsupported;
- start moving by rolling, wriggling and crawling;
- use a pincer grip;
- stand with support.

Spending time on the tummy helps babies to develop the muscles needed for crawling, walking and later movement.

Never leave your baby or child unattended in this position.

By 18 months, most children are able to:

- walk steadily without suddenly sitting down;
- kneel unsupported;
- move from a squatting position to standing;
- climb stairs with support;
- scribble with a pencil.

Give your baby lots of opportunities to crawl.

Crawling helps to co-ordinate the left and right and top and bottom of the body. It also helps to develop near-far focus as the baby has to keep looking up and down.

By the age of 3, most children are able to:

- walk and run forwards, backwards, sideways and on tip-toe;
- jump;
- stand on one foot;
- climb stairs;
- ride a tricycle;
- use a pencil, paintbrush and scissors.

Playing with large pulling and pushing toys helps to develop balance and co-ordination. Provide a range of materials, finger paints and crayons to develop creativity and fine motor control.

Enjoy a daily walk with your child whatever the weather! Provide safe opportunities for outdoor play and riding a trike. Share a book together and don't forget that jigsaw puzzles, junk modelling, drawing and painting are important for early learning.

Healthy Eating

We now realise that a healthy, balanced diet combined with regular exercise is necessary to develop both the body **and** the brain.

The brain contains millions of neurons and its growth is linked to the quality of nutrition in the early years. Rapid brain growth in early life means that children up to the age of two need a higher level of fat in their diets.

Babies should receive most of this fat from breast milk or formula during the first year of life. After this, it is important to provide a variety of foods, restricting fat, sugar and salt.

Eat plenty of fruit and vegetables.

Include bread, pasta, rice and cereals.

Provide plenty to drink every day.
Restrict sugary and fizzy drinks.

Getting the balance right with exercise, healthy nutrition, love and care will help you and your child to get the most out of life.

Keep Going

Young children naturally explore and interact with their world using movement. They need to do this feeling safe and secure within loving relationships.

The **Ready, Steady, Go!** Programme is based upon research that links physical movement with learning. It provides an opportunity to develop a close and trusting bond with your child as well as helping his or her brain development.

The human brain has an amazing capacity. It begins forming very early after conception and continues to develop rapidly during early childhood.

The following information is to help you understand how your child's brain works.

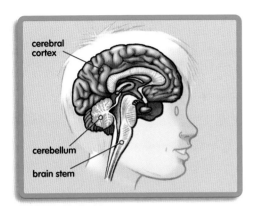

The brain stem, cerebellum and cerebral cortex form the three main parts of the brain.

Parts of the Brain

The **brain stem** links the brain to the spinal cord. It is responsible for basic life functions such as breathing, heartbeat, swallowing and consciousness. The primitive reflexes responsible for survival when a baby is born are also located here.

The **cerebellum** has a key role in enabling the child to control and refine movement so that he or she is able to walk, run, hop without thinking about it. The reflexes responsible for posture are also located here.

The **cerebral cortex** is responsible for processing information received through the senses and for speaking and thinking.

Babies and young children learn through seeing, hearing, touching, tasting and smelling. In addition to the five main senses, children need to develop balance and body awareness.

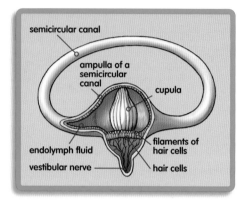

semicircular canal

ampulla of a
semicircular
canal

cupula

filaments of
hair cells

endolymph fluid

vestibular nerve

hair cells

Balance and Body Awareness

The Vestibular System

The inner ear contains the vestibular system, which is responsible for balance. The semi-circular canals contain fluid and tiny hairs which detect movement. A connection between the vestibular system and the eyes helps to maintain balance and keep the eyes focused on an object while the head is moving or while the body is rotating.

Proprioception

The proprioceptors are sensory receptors located in the muscles and joints. They pass information to the brain about the position of the body in space and the movements of parts of the body relative to each other. Adjustments to posture can therefore be made without thinking.

Music, Movement and Learning

It is no accident that the **Ready, Steady, Go!** movement programme is based around nursery rhymes. Research tells us that music and song have the power to stimulate and develop a child's intellectual, social, emotional, motor, language and communication skills.

A familiar song helps a baby to feel safe and secure as well as introducing him or her to the sounds and meanings of words. The rhythms and repetitive patterns of familiar nursery rhymes help to develop the memory providing fundamental building blocks necessary for effective learning.

Doing this fun programme for 5 to 10 minutes each day will help you to connect with your baby. You will find that the movements and songs come naturally. Enjoy the sessions and make the most of these golden opportunities to deepen the bond with your child so that he or she receives the best possible start in life.

Fascinated by this information?

Then why not **Keep Going** and find out more. On the next page, you will find details of some books and websites we have enjoyed.

Keep Going
Using the CD

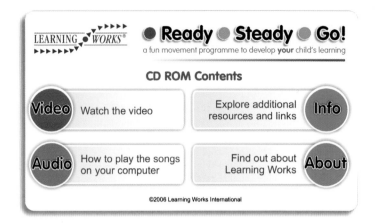

The **Ready, Steady, Go!** CD accompanying this book has a host of additional resources for you to explore and use.

Contents of **Ready, Steady, Go!** CD	
1. Meet the authors – video demonstration	Celia and Pat demonstrate four movements from the **Ready** Section of the book.
2. Music tracks for your **Ready, Steady, Go!** sessions	Each track starts with the words and music of the nursery rhyme and is then followed by the music only. This has been done to help you time each exercise and also to encourage participation by you and your child.
3. Ideas and play suggestions for you and your toddler	Master song sheets Exercise summary sheet Fingerplay rhymes Tongue Twisters 70 Play Ideas for you and your toddler
4. Websites for parents	27 websites and links for parents covering: health; twins and multiples; games; child development and parenting skills.

Ready, Steady, Go! Song List

Track	Title	Exercise	Page
Ready Section			
1 & **2**	Rock-a-bye baby	Rock-a-bye	4
3 & **4**	Pat-a-cake	Hello baby	5
5 & **6**	Two little dicky birds	Look and learn	6
7 & **8**	There were ten in the bed	Roly Poly	7
9 & **10**	See Saw Margery Daw	See Saw	8
11 & **12**	Ride a Cock Horse	Clippety Clop!	9
Steady Section			
13 & **14**	London Bridge	Rock and Roll	11
15 & **16**	Hickory, dickory dock	Touch and Count	12
17 & **18**	One, two, three, four, five	Touch and Count	12
19 & **20**	Bobby Shaftoe	Riding my bike	13
21 & **22**	Polly put the kettle on	Left Right	14
Go Section			
23 & **24**	Ring o' roses	Roundabout	16
25 & **26**	Row, row, row your boat	Row Boat	18
27 & **28**	Pop goes the weasel	Bouncy Ball	19
29 & **30**	Here we go round the Mulberry Bush	Circle Time	22
31 & **32**	The Grand Old Duke of York	Quick March	23

Keep Going
Ideas for further reading

Bee H. (2003)
The Developing Child   Allyn and Bacon

Eliot L. (1999)
Early Intelligence   Penguin

Gerhardt S. (2004)
Why love matters   Brunner-Routledge

Goddard Blythe S. (2004)
The Well Balanced Child   Hawthorn Press

Meggitt C. and Sunderland G. (2000)
Child Development: An Illustrated Guide   Heinemann

O'Donovan C J. (2003)
Helping Young Children to Learn through Movement
Lawrence Educational Publications

Websites

www.bbc.co.uk/parenting Visit this site for practical solutions to help with the challenges of everyday parenting.

www.parentlineplus.org.uk Parentline Plus is a UK registered charity which offers support, through an innovative range of free, flexible, responsive services, to anyone parenting a child.

www.surestart.gov.uk Sure Start is the UK Government's programme that aims to achieve better outcomes for children, parents and communities by positive action.

www.twinsandmultiples.org A website, produced by David Hay and Pat Preedy, which provides information, new knowledge and downloadable materials with regard to the educational needs of multiple birth children.

www.zerotothree.org ZERO TO THREE is an American non-profit making organisation whose mission is to promote the healthy development of infants and toddlers by supporting and strengthening families, communities, and those who work on their behalf.

Insert the CD into your computer's DVD/CD drive. Allow a few seconds for the menu to appear on your screen. Follow the instructions to play the music tracks, video or other parts of the disc.

Use the following method if the CD does not run.

Click on Start, Run, then type in: D:\setup.exe (substitute D for the letter of your DVD/CD drive if different) then click on OK.

Your CD is also ready to be played on your sound system at home or in the car.